Natural History Museum

Souvenir Guide

Welcome

Welcome to the Natural History Museum – for over 140 years we have been home to one of the world's most important natural history collections. Every year more than five million visitors are inspired by our unique collections and our beautiful building in South Kensington as they delight in the wonders of life on planet Earth. That life is under threat from global warming and biodiversity loss though, caused by the impact humans have had on natural habitats. And that is why, behind the scenes at the Museum, over 300 scientists are hard at work undertaking research into how we can do more to protect nature, control disease, and move to a green economy. We hope that your visit will inspire you to become an advocate for nature so that together we can look forward to a future in which both people and the planet thrive.

Doug Gurr
Director of the Natural History Museum

Contents

A gallery of life

The world-famous Natural History Museum in South Kensington, London, opened to the public on Easter Monday 18 April 1881. Designed as a 'cathedral to nature', the Museum's aim was to reveal the beauty and diversity of nature. In its first two weeks of being open, 40,000 people came to see the wonders of the natural world, displayed in a building as ornate as the animals and plants it housed. The Museum had a large introductory hall at its centre, from which led other galleries on geology, mineralogy, botany and zoology. Specimens large, small, familiar and exotic were displayed taxonomically, that is in groups of closely related individuals, reflecting the order of the world.

The Museum's aim, more than 135 years later, remains unchanged – to inspire a love of nature. Visitor numbers have grown to more than five million a year, as has the diversity of displays and activities on offer. People from across the world come to experience the programme of annual exhibitions, from world-class photography in *Wildlife Photographer of the Year* to explorations into colour, corals, extinction and whales. There are school workshops in the garden, virtual reality films, late openings and even the chance to spend the night here.

What some visitors may not know, is that since the glorious building with its blue and honey-coloured terracotta façade opened, it has held Britain's treasured natural history collections, some of the broadest of their kind in the world. They are an irreplaceable record of our planet's astonishing diversity, currently about 80 million objects strong. The beautiful, the rare, the revealing and the sometimes weird, these vast collections feed our knowledge of the natural world on which we all depend.

Only a fraction of the millions of objects we care for are on show. Behind the scenes lie kilometre after kilometre of shelving stacked with specimens in alcohol, from microscopic worms to formidable Komodo dragons. There are cupboards packed with pressed plants and freezers of frozen DNA. There are storerooms of skeletons of three-metre-long whale skulls and tiny boxes of fish bones, insects, historic maps, manuscripts and artworks, fossils, plants, minerals and meteorites. Among them are objects collected by some of the most famous names in natural history, and from the great voyages of discovery that opened up the natural world to westerners. There are fish and flowering plants from Captain James Cook's voyage on the *Endeavour* (1768–1771), a voyage to observe the transit of the planet Venus from Tahiti and to search for

BELOW The Natural History Museum was the first building in England to have a terracotta front, and it has become one of London's most recognisable and iconic landmarks.

the great southern continent, *Terra Australis Incognita*. And there are maps belonging to geology pioneers, like Charles Lyell (1797–1875), responsible for the idea that the Earth's surface was shaped by processes still at work today, and William 'Strata' Smith (1769–1839), who mapped out the different rock types of England and Wales.

The ever-growing collections are part of a global model of Earth's diversity, which the Museum looks after. They are an international resource, studied by over 350 scientists who work here and 11,000 visiting researchers a year. The specimens have a practical use too; they hold answers to some of the most pressing issues faced by humans today. Biodiversity loss, disease and climate change can all be studied using them. With objects spanning many thousands if not millions of years of Earth's history, they are a record of how our planet has changed, and a valuable indicator as to how it might change in the future.

ABOVE The original drawing of this woody pear, *Xylomelum pyriforme*, was made on the *Endeavour* voyage (1768–1771), by the young and talented artist Sydney Parkinson. An artist in London produced this watercolour by copying the original in 1773.

LEFT Charles Darwin was delighted and intrigued by the armadillos he saw in Argentina. The small armoured mammals were strikingly similar to some of the fossils he was encountering, seeming to be giant versions of the living species.

THE PICHI ARMADILLO,
DASYPUS MINUTUS.
Buenos Aires. Zaedyus pichiy
Presented by Charles Darwin, Esq., 1855.

Chocolate

How the Museum's collections began goes back to the seventeenth century, to a London doctor, naturalist and collector, Sir Hans Sloane (1660–1753). As a young man, Sloane's life was changed forever in 1687 when he went to work as the Governor of Jamaica's physician. During the fifteen months he spent there, he carefully recorded the island's natural history, returning to London with hundreds of plant and animal specimens. And so began the Museum's legacy.

Sloane rose to become President of the Royal Society, and the royal physician. But his public claim to fame is as the man who

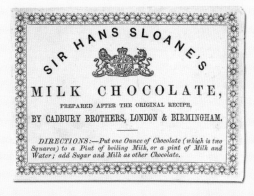

successfully marketed drinking chocolate in Britain. The Spanish had originally brought chocolate to Europe more than 100 years before, but it was Sloane who popularised it in Britain. While in Jamaica, he noticed local people brewed a bitter drink from the beans of the cacao tree. Finding it 'nauseous', he added hot milk and sugar and so created drinking chocolate. The scientific name for cacao is *Theobroma cacao*. *Theobroma* means drink of the gods although drinking chocolate was first sold as a medicine.

By the time he died in 1753, Sloane had amassed 80,000 objects and books. Ranging from natural history to archaeology the collection was so vast it filled his London home. He left it all to the nation in his will, and this was the seed of the British Museum in Bloomsbury, London, which opened in 1759. The collection was added to over the following years, and it soon became obvious that the natural history sections in particular were outgrowing their stores. Something would need to be done if what Sloane had left to the nation was to remain intact and seen by the public.

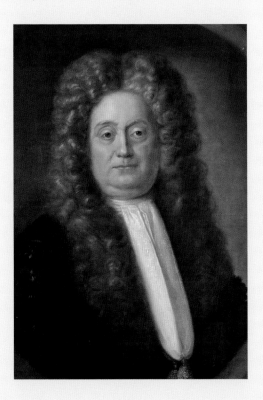

A temple to nature

The fate of the natural history section of Sloane's collection was determined by the appointment of a new superintendent for the British Museum's natural history departments, Sir Richard Owen, in 1856. This ambitious and accomplished scientist quickly identified that the collection was becoming cluttered and so he began a hard-fought campaign to persuade the trustees and government that a new, purpose-built building was needed.

In his new role, Sir Richard Owen watched as specimens poured in from colonies all over the world as Britain's empire expanded. The British Museum's natural history collections became ever more cramped and showed signs of neglect. Owen believed the world's most powerful nation, at that time, should have the world's biggest and best natural history museum. He wanted a new museum for them to showcase all these new finds, and the glory of God – to his mind, their creator.

Where this new museum should be built was hotly debated. At first it seemed unthinkable to move the collections from Bloomsbury, but after The Great Exhibition of 1851 in Hyde Park, South Kensington became a suitable option, earmarked as a centre for science and the arts. By 1864 the government had bought a site and hired the engineer Captain Francis Fowke to design the new museum. But plans were put on hold when Fowke died that same year, an event that led to the hiring of a relatively unknown but brilliant young architect Alfred Waterhouse. It was Waterhouse who would bring to life Owen's dream of creating a cathedral to nature, a faithful epitome of the natural world. Waterhouse rose to the challenge and created one of the finest Victorian buildings in England, using a round-arched Romanesque style, influenced in part by visits to German cathedrals.

The Museum is believed to be the first building to be clad inside and out with the combination of honey and pale

OPPOSITE These delicate, detailed and beautiful original drawings of a pair of herons and an ibex show how Waterhouse intended the finished terracotta motifs that would decorate the Museum to appear. They are anatomically and behaviourally correct.

BELOW Richard Owen (1804–1892), aged about 73 years old with the skeleton of a giant moa. He famously identified the moa from only a fragment of leg bone.

blue terracotta, made from baked clay. Terracotta was chosen because it is cheap and easy to clean, and can be moulded. Waterhouse created wonderful depictions of plants and animals to decorate the building, described by *The Times* on opening 'as befits a Palace of Nature', a temple of God's work. The decorations were carefully checked by Owen, and reflected his plan to divide the Museum displays rigorously between past and present, with living creatures to the west, fossils, rocks and minerals to the east. Once approved, Waterhouse's drawings were sent to an architectural modelling company, Farmer and Brindley, where they were modelled by Monsieur Du Jardin and cast by Gibbs and Canning of Tamworth. The more elaborate figures were cast once and appear in only one location, while more basic motifs were cast multiple times and are repeated throughout the building. On columns and arches, birds and mammals peer out from foliage, while octopuses and fish float in rippling waves.

The foundation stone was laid in 1873, construction continued throughout the 1870s, and by mid-1880 the building was complete. Named the British Museum (Natural History), this palace of mosaic floors and wrought iron opened to the public in 1881. Moving the natural history collections to South Kensington from Bloomsbury took more than a year. Last to arrive, in late 1882, were the zoological collections, a move that took 97 days and 394 trips by horse and cart. Among them were 52,000 fragile glass bottles of fish and other animals preserved in highly flammable methylated spirit, which were stored in a specially built secure building at the back of the Museum. In 2002, these collections were moved again to a safer, environmentally controlled building called the Darwin Centre, and by then they numbered 22 million items.

OPPOSITE The Darwin Centre's Cocoon provides controlled conditions for storing the Museum's astonishing collection of insects, arachnids and plant specimens.

BELOW The whole Museum building is covered with hundreds of fantastic terracotta animals and plants, living and extinct.

The largest move in the Museum's history was yet to come. In 2005 about 28 million insect and spider specimens were packed up and the 1930s building that housed them was demolished to make way for their new home, the second part of the Darwin Centre. The Darwin Centre is a state-of-the-art laboratory and storage facility for 28 million entomology, 22 million zoology and six million plant specimens. At its heart is a 65-metre-long, eight-storey-high cocoon, completed in 2009, of 3,500 square metres of hand-finished polished plaster, bound in steel channels resembling silk threads.

Hintze Hall

Sir Richard Owen's vision to create a spectacular overview of the natural world is perhaps most evident in Hintze Hall, an exhibit in itself. Light streaming in through the high windows picks out details in its terracotta decorations, stained glass and mosaic floor. Wide, round-arched bays along each side house some of the Museum's many treasures.

The hall has undergone several iterations since Owen's day, but his core aim, that it be an iconic introduction to nature, persists. At its centre suspended from the ceiling is a blue whale, *Balaenoptera musculus*, skeleton. This 25-metre female beached on Swanton's Bank on 26 March 1891, near the mouth of Wexford Harbour in Ireland. The carcass was bought by a merchant, who extracted more than 2,800 litres of whale oil from it to sell for a large profit. The Museum bought the skeleton in 1891, then in 1934 it was suspended in the newly constructed *Mammals* gallery. Moving it to Hintze Hall has given scientists the opportunity to study the skeleton while off display, scanning the bones and extracting new data for scientific research.

The whale is named 'Hope' to highlight the powerful story she tells about man's relationship with the natural world. By the middle of the twentieth century the blue whale was on the brink of extinction. Its population had declined from 250,000 a century earlier to only a few hundred. At a meeting of the International Whaling Commission in 1966, a decision was taken to protect the great whales, one of the first times mankind acted on a global scale to save another species. Today, as a result of that action, there are about 20,000 blue whales and they are again playing a crucial role in sustaining the ecosystem and habitat in which they live.

There are many other icons on display in Hintze Hall, housed in ten alcoves that line each side of the hall, known as wonder bays. Among them is a piece of banded rock, more than three billion years old. Its intricate and dramatic layers signal a turning point in Earth's history – the increase of atmospheric oxygen, one of the key components

ABOVE Detail of a terracotta panel showing a European fox with a cub and bird, designed by Alfred Waterhouse.

OPPOSITE This specimen of an America mastodon, *Mammut americanum*, was acquired by the Museum in 1844. Mastodons are often confused with mammoths but mastodons were slightly smaller and had shorter, gently curved tusks, whereas mammoths had very high shoulders, a sloping back and twisted tusks. Elephants aren't direct descendants of mammoths or mastodons though they share a common ancestor.

LEFT Giraffes are the tallest living animal; their long necks are perfectly suited to feeding on the tall bushes and shrubs that are beyond the reach of other species on the African savannahs. Remarkably, a giraffe's neck contains the same number of bones as a human's. Gradual natural selection over many generations has led to the bones becoming much longer. They are social animals and roam around in groups, called towers, of around 15, led by one male.

in the evolution of life on this planet. A *Mantellisaurus* skeleton, discovered on the Isle of Wight, is one of the most complete dinosaurs ever found in the UK. There's an American mastodon from Missouri, USA probably 40,000 to 30,000 years old, and thought to have been brought to extinction by a combination of climate change, habitat loss and hunting by humans. And an efficient predator in even the deep, cold parts of the ocean, a blue marlin, *Makaira nigricans,* which has the ability to generate heat in its eye muscles to warm its huge eyes and brain.

Smaller icons are also represented. Although tiny, insects make up more than 50 per cent of known species on Earth and are an essential part of all land-based ecosystems. With nearly a million named species and many more awaiting discovery, insects are the largest and most diverse group of living animals. Specimens from each of the orders, or groups, of living insects and their close relatives are on display. Their immense physical diversity has evolved over time from a relatively simple body plan. The Natural History Museum houses more than 37 million insects, representing more than half the known species.

OVERLEAF The 25.2 metre-long female skeleton of the blue whale, *Balaenoptera musculus*, named Hope has been hanging in Hintze Hall since July 2017. The blue whale is the largest animal ever to have lived and Hope is so called to highlight the powerful story she tells about man's relationship with the natural world.

ABOVE Red seaweed is a close relative of land plants and has long been a source of food for humans and livestock. The Museum's seaweed collection has more than 200,000 specimens.

BELOW Sedimentary rocks like this banded iron formation formed in shallow water millions of years ago. The intricate layers are composed of silt and oxidised iron, proving an increase in atmospheric oxygen.

Beyond Hintze Hall

Two balconies overlook Hintze Hall. On the eastern balcony are minerals and rocks. The Natural History Museum's mineral collection has more than 180,000 specimens, making it one of the largest and most comprehensive in the world, a diverse group of form, colour and chemical composition. Minerals can be simple in structure but dramatic in appearance. It is their visual appeal that makes polished and cut minerals so desirable. Rocks comprise one or more minerals, and form our planet's solid outer layer, the lithosphere. The Natural History Museum's decorative rock collection is used to identify natural stone in historic buildings, assisting in the conservation and repair work of our urban heritage.

Birds also feature on this floor, to the west. Charles Darwin, fearing their often extreme colour, ornament, weapons and behaviour contradicted his theory of natural selection, was the first to suggest that decoration in particular must evolve to improve mating success, and the male pheasants on display illustrate this perfectly with their ornamental feathers. Also exhibited are parrots from South America, one of the richest areas in the world for birds. Although they appear remarkably different, all species of South American parrot diverged from one family. The combination of mountains and tropical forests creates an ideal environment for the formation of new species, each adapted to particular habitats, climates or foods. Southern seabirds feature too – the albatross, shearwaters and petrels – illustrating how a single group of birds has evolved to exploit different lifestyles. With their extraordinary wingspan the large albatross are adapted to soaring high over the waves, while the two smaller species have shorter wings designed to flutter along, or dive below the surface. At their breeding sites all are vulnerable to predators and human disturbance, while at sea they are threatened by the fishing industry.

Only by carefully preparing and storing specimens in the collection can we preserve them for future generations to enjoy and study. Skinning, mounting and stuffing, pickling, pressing and drying are all methods of preservation. Stuffing, or taxidermy, is perfect for display,

ABOVE The West Balcony displays explore the diversity of bird species, including dozens of pheasants such as these (from top): Bornean crested fireback, Sebright bantam cockerel and golden pheasant, included with their female counterparts to show the dramatic diversity of plumage that has evolved in male pheasants, highlighting the extreme sexual dimorphism in this group.

demonstrating what an animal might have looked like in life. Pickling or drying are ideal for scientific research as they preserve almost every element of the organism for future study.

On the second floor balcony stands one of the Museum's most impressive exhibits, a single massive slice taken from a giant sequoia, one of the world's largest trees. When living, this tree stood at more

than 60 metres, taller than the Museum's tallest tower. We know it was 1,300 years old when it was cut down as someone counted all its growth rings. On a panel underneath the trunk some famous events in history are marked, including the beginning of the Islamic calendar in 622 when the human population was just 206 million, and the publication of Charles Darwin's *On the Origin of Species* in 1859, when the population had exceeded one billion. It was a seedling in 557, and 500 years later was already more than two metres wide. Uncut, it might have continued growing for another 1,000 years. Sequoias are some of the largest and longest living trees in the world, and remarkably they grow from seeds no bigger than a grain of wheat.

The five-metre-wide slice comes from a tree felled specially for the Chicago World Fair in 1893, when such trees were more common than today. They now grow only in the Sierra Nevada Mountains of central California and are highly protected. Nowadays it would be unthinkable to cut one down for an exhibition.

The sequoia isn't the only impressive feature of this elevated point. It is the closest you can get to one of Waterhouse's most beautiful additions, a magnificent painted gilded canopy. Spanning the length of Hintze Hall, the ceiling is made up of 162 panels of flowering plants, painted by the firm Best & Lea of Manchester. The ceiling served Waterhouse's aim to 'clothe over practical necessities with such beauty as they were capable of receiving' and, given his designs were inspired by churches and cathedrals, it is easy to find a resemblance between the Museum's richly adorned Hintze Hall ceiling and that of Renaissance masterpieces such as the Sistine Chapel.

The plants depicted are a mixture of the familiar and the exotic, and represent both the trade and culture of the time. There is an English oak, *Quercus robur*, and a Scots pine, *Pinus sylvestris*, both cultural

BELOW, OPPOSITE AND OPPOSITE BOTTOM The plants on the gloriously decorated ceiling panels are a mix of native species and those from far-away countries. There are very few records of who painted them and why they were chosen. Shown here are the greater spearwort, *Ranunculus lingua* (below), the magnificent ceiling of the Museum's Hintze Hall (opposite) and Iris, *Iris* cf. *germanica* (opposite bottom).

icons. There are fruiting species from southern Europe, among them oranges and lemons. There are figs and olives, pomegranates and grapes, to us quite common now but to the Victorians these plants held classical, even biblical relevance.

There are also species that represent the British Empire, such as tobacco, cotton, coffee, tea, sugarcane, nutmeg and chocolate, *Theobroma cacao*, perhaps a tribute to Sir Hans Sloane whose collections form the heart of the Museum. And the ornamentals that made European gardens bloom, such as rhododendrons, dogrose and honeysuckle, are also included in meticulous detail.

Treasures – Cadogan Gallery

Treasures is an intimate celebration of the Museum's collection, twenty-two specially selected objects that are either unique, valuable, famous or surprising. Selecting a few objects from a collection of 80 million objects is a near-impossible task, but each is special in its own way. They were chosen from the earth and life sciences departments – palaeontology, botany, zoology, mineralogy and entomology – and include specimens from the voyages by Charles Darwin and Captain James Cook. There are rocks from beyond our planet, such as the oldest surviving meteorite discovered in the UK, formed during the birth of the solar system 4.6 billion years ago, and a piece of Moon presented to the Museum by President Nixon. There's the first Neanderthal skull discovered and the first *Iguanodon* teeth ever found. There's also the first *Archaeopteryx* ever discovered, one of only eleven specimens known worldwide of probably the earliest known bird.

Pieces worked by human hand are very rare among the collection, making the delicate nautilus shell carved by Johannes Belkien in the late 1600s particularly prized. It is from the collection of Sir

ABOVE This exquisite ornament, the size of a human eye, has a stunning, rose-cut, deep-blue sapphire as its centrepiece. It has been in the Museum's collections for more than 250 years.

LEFT Sloane collected all manner of unusual things, including antiquities, manuscripts and items such as this beautifully carved nautilus shell, which formed one of the founding objects of the Museum.

Louisiana Heron. ARDEA LUDOVICIANA; *Male adult*

Hans Sloane, which itself formed the foundation of the Museum. The nautilus is considered a living fossil, having remained relatively unchanged since the appearance of its ancestors 350 million years ago. Today the nautilus suffers from overfishing due to the continuing popularity of its shell's distinctive shape and lustre.

Artworks form a huge part of the Museum's collection, and one of the most spectacular is a page from *The Birds of America* by John James Audubon (1785–1851), an American ornithologist and artist. The metre-long hand-coloured prints are full of drama and life, each bird pictured life-size in its natural habitat. The stuffed specimens painted by Audubon's contemporaries looked lifeless and unnatural by comparison.

ABOVE Instead of working from prepared skins or captive birds in zoos like many of his contemporaries, Audubon travelled America to see them in the wild and was determined to depict birds in their natural habitat and at full size, like this Louisiana heron.

No natural history collection would be complete without a dodo, and the Museum looks after a rare skeleton, constructed from bones compiled from different individuals and around 1,000 years old. Just 90 years after humans discovered the dodo on the island of Mauritius off the east coast of Africa, in the late 1500s, these docile birds were extinct. To investigate the origins of this unusual species, the Museum's first superintendent Sir Richard Owen intercepted some rare dodo specimens that were being sent to a potential rival in 1866, and thus the bones became part of the Museum's collection. Owen was the first person to publish a scientific description of the dodo based on these bones.

ABOVE This emperor penguin egg was collected along with two others and their embryos on Captain Scott's *Terra Nova* expedition (1910–1913).

BELOW The dodo was driven to extinction by the arrival of humans on the island of Mauritius. No complete dodo skeletons exist from a single individual.

One of three emperor penguin eggs brought back from the Antarctic by Captain Scott's tragic polar expedition is also on display, collected to try to prove that birds and reptiles were related to each other. Edward Wilson, chief scientist of Scott's 1910 *Terra Nova* expedition to Antarctica, walked 100 kilometres in complete darkness and in temperatures down to −40°C to retrieve eggs at different stages of development, from what was then the only known emperor penguin breeding colony. The three eggs that survived the journey were cut open, and their embryos were removed and pickled when they got back to camp. By the time of their eventual study in 1934, the theory responsible for their collection had been dismissed.

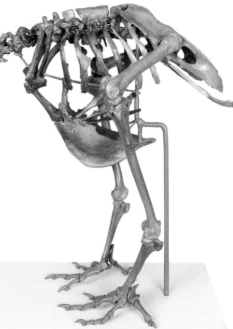

Books are among the many treasures of the Museum, and perhaps none more so in natural history circles than a first edition of Charles Darwin's *On the Origin of Species*, published in 1859. In it Darwin describes his theory of evolution by means of natural selection. Despite the controversy surrounding the theory at the time, the book sold out the day it was published. Its success may have in part been due to its conversational rather than academic writing style. Darwin was galvanised into publishing earlier than planned after receiving a letter outlining a similar theory from fellow naturalist Alfred Russel Wallace.

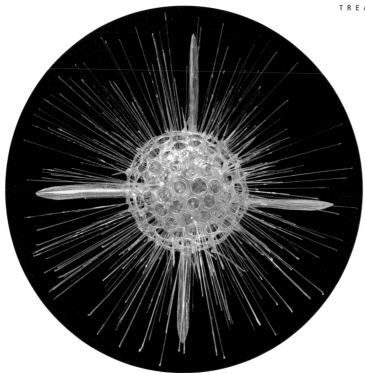

Treasured too are reconstructions, among the most prized an exquisitely accurate glass model of a microscopic radiolarian, made by Leopold Blaschka and his son Rudolph between 1876 and 1889. Leopold was inspired to recreate marine creatures in glass after a long sea voyage. Ranging from octopuses to microscopic plankton, the Blaschkas' work was popular with museums, which had previously struggled to display these creatures as the animals lack backbones, and so tended to sink to the bottom of their display jars. No one has been able to replicate the Blaschkas' techniques.

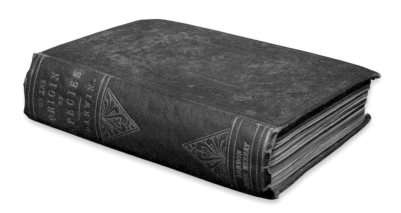

ABOVE Exceptionally intricate, this detailed glass model of a radiolarian is part of a set made for the Natural History Museum in the second half of the nineteenth century and has enormous scientific value.

LEFT *On the Origin of Species* is one of the most influential books ever written. Charles Darwin knew it would be controversial to suggest that species evolved gradually and naturally, without the intervention of a divine authority.

Dinosaurs

Dinosaurs are a group of reptiles, which includes their living descendants, the birds. All dinosaurs walked with straight legs tucked underneath them rather than sprawling to the sides like lizards. For 160 million years, between 230 and 66 million years ago, dinosaurs dominated the land with an astonishing array of forms. To date more than 1,000 species of extinct dinosaur have been discovered from sites all over the world: long-necked plant-eaters, powerful predators and smaller, swifter pack hunters. The largest creatures ever to live on land were dinosaurs, but some are no bigger than a hummingbird.

ABOVE This is the tooth of *Iguanodon*, one of the first dinosaurs to have been discovered. The first fossilised teeth of this species were found by a roadside in Sussex, England in 1822.

BELOW The fast-moving *Velociraptor* was a hunter with powerful claws and needle-sharp teeth. It had short fine feathers on its torso and larger ones on its arms, tail and head.

Dinosaurs have captured our imagination since the first monstrous fossils were identified in the nineteenth century, and it was the Museum's first superintendent, Sir Richard Owen, who invented the term dinosaur, in 1842. Since then, piecing together how they lived and moved has taken intense research and many questions still remain. *Tyrannosaurus rex*, at first thought to be a terrifying predator due to its huge jaws, three times as powerful as a lion's, is now thought to have also scavenged – too slow and cumbersome to always hunt down its own dinner. Scientists can learn about these prehistoric beasts from bones, skulls and teeth, tracks and even droppings. How their joints articulate can reveal how they moved, an impression in rock gives us a clue to skin patterning, head structures hint at sounds they could have made and a fossilised nest of eggs suggests how they looked after their young. All this evidence put together helps to bring extinct dinosaurs back to life.

With the exception of their direct descendants, the birds, the other dinosaurs became extinct about 66 million years ago. Many experts agree that a massive meteorite striking Earth may have wiped out the dinosaurs, but alongside this sudden catastrophe many other natural events were happening too. Sea levels were falling at the time of the impact, and simultaneously intense volcanic eruptions were throwing out poison gases and darkening the skies. The combined effect was enough to kill all of the non-bird dinosaurs.

The Museum has one of the finest collections of dinosaur material in the world, including some of the earliest dinosaur fossils ever described. These are the strange iguana-like teeth collected by Mary and Gideon Mantell in 1822, and the Maidstone slab, a partial skeleton bought for Mantell by his friends in 1834. He originally named both sets of remains *Iguanodon*, but the animal in the Maidstone slab is now called *Mantellisaurus* in his honour.

In 1983, Museum scientists unearthed one of the most complete skeletons of a meat-eating dinosaur found in Europe. It was later named *Baryonyx walkeri* after William Walker, an amateur fossil hunter who found its claw. Its unusually long skull was armed with teeth well-suited to catching and gripping fish, and it may have used its great hand claw to hook fish out of the water.

One of the most precious fossils in the collection shows the transition dinosaurs made to birds, an ancient bird with feathers but also with reptilian features such as claws and teeth. Called *Archaeopteryx*, it was bought by Sir Richard Owen, and only twelve fossils of this unique, 150-million-year-old creature have ever been found. Over the next century, other feathered fossils have emerged, especially from China. Some were clearly fast-running dinosaurs with a feathery covering, from which most scientists now agree birds evolved. Dinosaurs and birds share a remarkable biological past. A spectacular fossil record shows how small, feathered, bipedal, predatory dinosaurs (called theropods) such as *Deinonychus* evolved into birds 160 million years ago. These fossils show the evolutionary transitions: how a deep, toothy snout became a

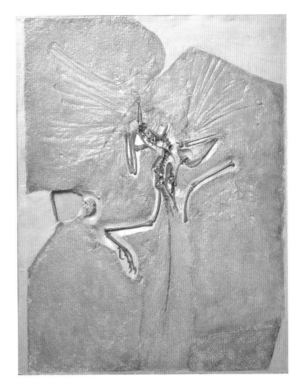

ABOVE *Archaeopteryx* is the first definitive bird and this fossil is one of the most valuable in the Museum's collection.

BELOW Discovered in a quarry in southern England, this enormous claw – 30.5 cm (12 in) long – belonged to the dinosaur *Baryonyx walkeri*.

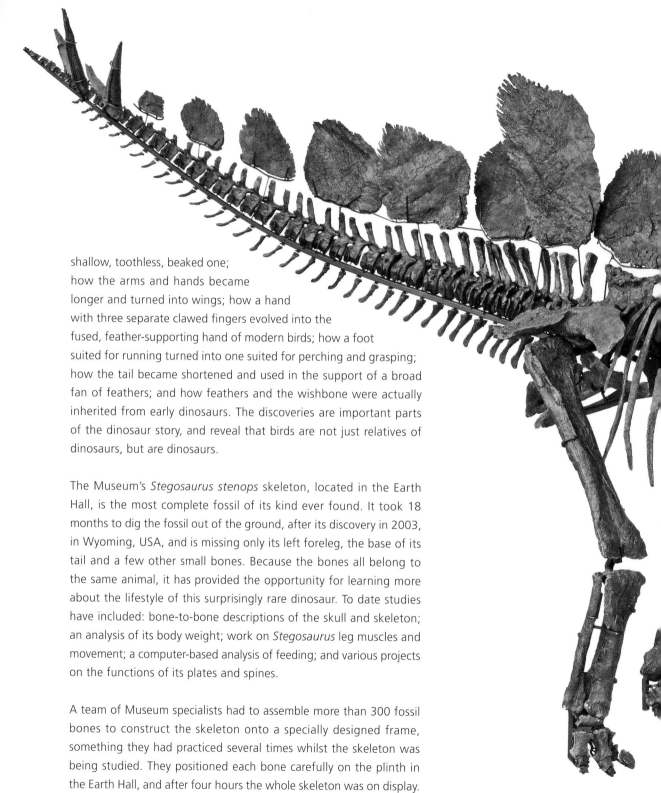

shallow, toothless, beaked one;
how the arms and hands became
longer and turned into wings; how a hand
with three separate clawed fingers evolved into the
fused, feather-supporting hand of modern birds; how a foot
suited for running turned into one suited for perching and grasping;
how the tail became shortened and used in the support of a broad
fan of feathers; and how feathers and the wishbone were actually
inherited from early dinosaurs. The discoveries are important parts
of the dinosaur story, and reveal that birds are not just relatives of
dinosaurs, but are dinosaurs.

The Museum's *Stegosaurus stenops* skeleton, located in the Earth
Hall, is the most complete fossil of its kind ever found. It took 18
months to dig the fossil out of the ground, after its discovery in 2003,
in Wyoming, USA, and is missing only its left foreleg, the base of its
tail and a few other small bones. Because the bones all belong to
the same animal, it has provided the opportunity for learning more
about the lifestyle of this surprisingly rare dinosaur. To date studies
have included: bone-to-bone descriptions of the skull and skeleton;
an analysis of its body weight; work on *Stegosaurus* leg muscles and
movement; a computer-based analysis of feeding; and various projects
on the functions of its plates and spines.

A team of Museum specialists had to assemble more than 300 fossil
bones to construct the skeleton onto a specially designed frame,
something they had practiced several times whilst the skeleton was
being studied. They positioned each bone carefully on the plinth in
the Earth Hall, and after four hours the whole skeleton was on display.

BELOW *Stegosaurus* lived around 150 million years ago. A slow-moving plant-eater, it would have used its four vicious tail spikes as protection against other dinosaur predators. This *Stegosaurus* was a young adult when it died.

Fossil marine reptiles

The fish-like ichthyosaurs, paddle-limbed plesiosaurs and shorter-necked pliosaurs, mosasaurs and marine crocodiles were all once powerful predators. Although now extinct, they lived during the time dinosaurs dominated the land, and one of the most famous fossil hunters of these great beasts was English fossil collector Mary Anning (1799–1847). Despite being a female in a male-dominated industry, she found her first ichthyosaur at the age of 11, in the cliffs along the Dorset coast in England where she lived. The counties of Dorset and Somerset are especially rich in marine fossils, because the sediments containing them – formed from ancient seabeds – are exposed in quarries and cliffs. It was Anning who discovered the first almost complete ichthyosaur, plesiosaur and pterosaur fossils ever found in Britain. She built a thriving business selling fossils, and her reputation as a collector and expert grew. Anning was consulted by many of the leading scientists of the day, such as English geologist William Buckland (1784–1856), the first man to give a name to a dinosaur – *Megalosaurus*. Some of Anning's correspondence is kept in our Library and Archives.

ABOVE Mary Anning is pictured in her outdoor clothing with her faithful dog, geological hammer and fossil-collecting basket. She inspired the tongue-twister 'She sells seashells on the sea shore'.

BELOW The long-snouted ichthyosaur, *Leptopterygius tenuirostris,* swam in the seas more than 200 million years ago. This fossil was found in Somerset, England.

The ichthyosaurs, meaning fish lizards, were the dolphins of their day, swift and deadly hunters with large eyes and long, sharp-toothed jaws. Like dolphins, they gave birth to live young in the water. We know this from fossils that show embryos in the bodies of adults. One fossil appears to capture the moment of birth itself, the baby just expelled from its mother's body.

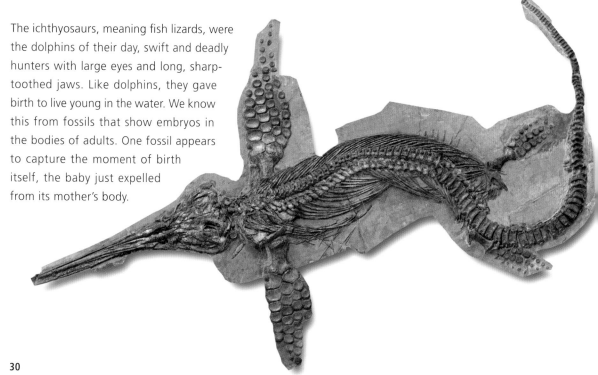

The ground sloth

Among these marine predators stands another giant, not of the ocean but of the land, and one of the most photographed specimens in the Museum. The four-metre-high replica skeleton is of the ground sloth *Megatherium*. Voyaging scientists such as Charles Darwin brought the curious bones of these mammoth beasts back to Europe. Richard Owen described and named many of them, including *Megatherium* and *Glyptodon*, the tank-like giant armadillo. *Megatherium* was a land mammal with long shaggy fur, foot-long claws and long arms and was one of several gigantic plant-eaters that lived in South America between 100,000 and 11,000 years ago, a time when the north was gripped in a series of ice ages. Initially it was thought to have walked on all four legs, but it was realised that in fact it reared up on its massive legs, pulling down branches of trees to feed its great bulk.

Birds

Birds are warm-blooded vertebrates that lay hard-shelled eggs and have feathers. Their forelimbs are modified as wings and most can fly, but some have lost the ability to do so and some, like the penguins, 'fly' through water rather than air. Of all the birds, perhaps the dodo is the most famous, remembered more for its rapid extinction rather than its life history. This large flightless bird, closely related to pigeons, was discovered on the Indian Ocean island of Mauritius off the east coast of Africa by Europeans in 1598, and was probably wiped out by the late 1660s. It had no defence against the hunters and the animals brought by them to the island – especially pigs, rats and monkeys, which attacked their eggs and young.

ABOVE Passenger pigeons, *Ectopistes migratorius*, lived in eastern North America and went from being one of the most common birds alive, with a population numbering hundreds of millions, to extinction in less than 100 years.

LEFT Early dodo reconstructions were usually short and dumpy, as shown here, but scientists now think they would have been slimmer and stood much more upright. Their feathers were similar to those of a pigeon, and they had a powerful beak adapted for crushing tough fruits, seeds, shells and crustaceans.

Bird jewels

Hummingbirds are among the jewels of the bird group, and among the Museum's collection is a large wooden case full of them, dating from the early 1800s. The tiny, brightly-coloured hummingbirds astonished the Victorians, and a huge trade grew in their skins. Prolonged exposure to light fades most of the iridescent feathers to brown, but some still flash with colour.

Remarkably few skin remains of dodos exist, but new fossil material, including rare items such as a dodo beak and bones of young dodos, has been discovered by a Dutch–Mauritian research team. It is hoped that this new evidence will reveal what life was like for the dodo before humans arrived, and will help us to understand more about extinction events on Mauritius and other oceanic islands.

Perhaps the most intriguing aspect of these animals is their egg. This perfectly packaged home for the developing chick contains all the food it will need, enveloped in a tough membrane, inside a shell that allows air both in and out. The largest egg in the world was laid by the now extinct 400 kilogramme elephant bird of Madagascar – its egg is bigger than any dinosaur egg yet discovered. The smallest known egg is laid by the vervain hummingbird, no bigger than the fingernail on a little finger.

The Museum holds over 300,000 sets of bird eggs, in total over a million individual eggs and nests in our collections together with their collection data. They are especially important to science as a source of information on the lives and past distributions of bird populations. Scientists use them to study the timing of the seasonal laying of eggs and whether this is affected by climate change and other factors. They can also check whether a species' range has changed by examining where the nests were found.

BELOW Objects such as eggs show considerable variation. Barely the size of a pea, the world's smallest egg laid by a living bird, the blue-tailed emerald hummingbird, *Chlorostilbon mellisugus*, is shown here with one of the largest, that of the common ostrich, *Struthio camelus*.

Mammals

A mammal, like us, is a four-limbed, warm-blooded creature with fur or hair, one that gives birth to live young and suckles them with milk. However, there are exceptions that have evolved to fit a wide range of niches. The platypus is a mammal but it still lays eggs, while dolphins have no fur and bats have wings instead of front legs. But they all share the same basic body plan and physiology.

The first mammals evolved 220 million years ago, but remained small and insignificant during the reign of the dinosaurs. When dinosaurs went extinct, the diversity of mammals on Earth exploded. Many of their competitors and predators had disappeared and they took advantage of this – several types of mammal appeared for the first time immediately afterwards in a greater variety of forms and sizes. The many forms we know today are relatively recent in Earth's history. The most famous in the collection is probably the blue whale model.

Almost 30 metres long, it was constructed on site in the *Mammals* gallery in 1938 and modelled on beached whales, without the benefit of modern underwater photography. We now know the whale is usually much sleeker in life and the flexible throat is fully extended only when feeding. The blue whale is the largest animal to have ever lived. It has a heart the size of a small family car, with arteries like drainpipes.

Other species of cetacean – whales, dolphins and porpoises – are regularly stranded along our shores. In 1913 the Crown granted the Museum scientific research rights for the collection of data on the 'fishes royal'. Since then the Museum has been central to the monitoring of strandings in British waters, and more than 12,000 have been recorded, including some new species. The Museum plays an important role in the collaborative UK Cetacean Strandings Investigation Programme, which is a vital part of nationwide research into the status of cetacean populations around the UK. Studies of strandings help us to understand their diversity, distribution and any

BELOW Our life-size blue whale model was built to astound and educate. Assembled in place and hanging from the ceiling, it has a wooden frame, which is coated in wire mesh and plaster of Paris.

threats to their survival from pollution, fishing or disease. The Museum currently processes reports of around 500 strandings per year.

Among the most enigmatic of mammals is the elephant, which evolved over 40 million years from the strange little barrel-bodied *Moeritherium*, with only the hint of a trunk. The elephant's relatives, the spectacular mammoths, were hunted by early humans, possibly to extinction, and it too is equally vulnerable today. The Museum holds a pair of elephant trophy tusks, the largest in the world, a moving reminder of the threat posed by humans. Today, elephants, rhinos, hippos and many other species are protected, but poaching continues. Habitat loss and the encroachment of human populations threaten the larger, slower-breeding mammal species most.

ABOVE These are the heaviest tusks ever recorded, each weighing about 100 kilogrammes, about the same as ten car tyres, and they are more than three metres long. They belonged to an unusually large male elephant killed near Mount Kilimanjaro, Tanzania in the 1890s.

LEFT Chi-Chi the giant panda was caught as a young cub in the mountains of western China, the only place giant pandas live in the wild. She was a favourite at London Zoo for 14 years and when she died in 1972, her skin was given to the Museum and she was stuffed and displayed feeding on bamboo.

OPPOSITE African elephants are the world's largest land animals, but these wonderful animals remain under severe threat from poaching and habitat loss.

Fish, amphibians and reptiles

From hairy frogs and human-eating crocodiles to fish that make their own light, fish, amphibians and reptiles are the most ancient vertebrates on Earth, and some of the most endangered. This group illustrates life's transition, over hundreds of millions of years, from a watery existence to life on land. Considered by some to be less charismatic than their warm-blooded relatives, they are nevertheless highly successful survivors from long before mammals and birds emerged. There are almost as many fish species alive today as all the birds, reptiles, amphibians and mammals combined.

The deep-sea fish show just how curious life can get. This vast region, 2,000 to 5,000 metres below the surface, is one of the least explored areas on our planet. Many strange creatures exist here that are quite unlike anything found nearer the surface. There are fish that never see the light of day, so make their own. Some hunt with lures on inbuilt 'fishing rods', and others swallow meals as big as themselves. Here

ABOVE The shell of a tortoise is made up of two parts – the upper carapace and the bottom plastron. Both are made of many fused bones and get bigger with the tortoise as it grows.

BELOW LEFT The football fish, *Himantolophus groenlandicus*, lives in the dark depths of the ocean. Females have a luminescent lantern protruding from their heads which they use to attract prey.

OPPOSITE Discovered as recently as 1912, the Komodo dragon, *Varanus komodoensis*, is the largest lizard living today, and is only found on a cluster of rocky and desolate Indonesian islands, east of Bali. This specimen is 259 cm long.

at the Museum we look after one of the largest and most important collections of deep-sea creatures in the world. They play a vital role in helping us to map the sea's diversity.

Among this group of vertebrates are many record holders, from the whale shark that can grow to 15 metres long to West Africa's goliath frog, a dull green frog with a yellow underside, which can grow as big as a house cat and has large webbed hind feet and is a powerful swimmer. The largest lizard on Earth joins them, the infamous Komodo dragon with saliva that contains strains of deadly bacteria causing its prey to die of blood poisoning after being bitten. The dragons then use their extraordinary sense of smell to track down the corpse of their prey. The Museum also holds some curiosities from this group, including a huge crocodile with some of the contents of its last meal, a tortoise skeleton split in two showing how its backbone and ribs fuse to form the protective shell, a snake swallowing an egg whole, an amphibian that reaches adulthood without undergoing metamorphosis, and a tadpole three times larger than the frog into which it grows.

Fish, with hardly an exception, are water-bound, while most reptiles can live their whole lives as air-breathers on land. But amphibians lead a double life, as anyone with a garden pond will know. Frogs, toads and newts go through a quite astonishing transformation during their life cycle, from water-living tadpoles to air-breathing adults. Some species show strange variations on this theme – the eggs can be carried in pockets on the mother's back, brooded by the male in its vocal sac or, as with the midwife toad, wrapped round the male's hind legs.

ABOVE Male hairy frogs, *Trichobatrachus robustus*, develop fine hair-like growths of skin during breeding season. These hairs are thought to help the male to absorb more oxygen during this period of increased activity.

Marine invertebrates

The marine invertebrates, creatures without a backbone, inhabit the oceans that cover two-thirds of the planet's surface. Many are startlingly beautiful, and the temptation throughout history to collect them now threatens many with extinction. The Museum looks after about 23 million marine invertebrate specimens, ranging from the gigantic to creatures too tiny to see without a microscope. There are sponges, corals, worms, sea urchins, squids, octopuses, hard-shelled molluscs and crustaceans. Curious creatures include tiny animals called bryozoans that live in immobile colonies, though some are able to move around on the sea-bed using stilt-like bristles. There are sea stars with a basketful of arms, and parasitic worms that wind their way round the guts of marine fish.

One of the most beautiful is a group of sponges called the Venus' flower baskets. What you see in the specimens are their bleached 'skeletons', delicate lattices of microscopic six-armed silica spicules. Many species of sponge are identified by the shape of their spicules, which survive far better than soft parts. At the Museum, there are 60 per cent of the world's type specimens of sponges, those precious individuals used to define each species.

Corals are invertebrates, and the reefs they form are physically tough structures – the devastating 2004 tsunami in Asia could not shake them. But they are vulnerable to pollution, sea warming, the effects of tourism and over-harvesting for sale. International treaties ban the trade in endangered corals, but the business is lucrative and smuggling continues. When police and customs intercept large hauls of coral destined for the commercial market they bring them to the Museum for identification. We use the reference collections to check if any are endangered.

ABOVE Glass sponges are common animals in the deep sea and have a skeleton made of silica, which is the same material used to make glass.

BELOW This carnivorous marine Venus comb snail lives in the shallow waters of the Indian Ocean and the Pacific as far as Fiji. It crawls on the muddy seabed, channelling water through the thin end of its shell, the siphonal canal. The siphon helps the snail 'smell' the water around it, picking up chemical signals from nearby predators or prey.

OPPOSITE This coral sea fan, *Gorgonia flabellum*, is found in the shallow waters of the Caribbean. It can grow to more than 1.5 metres tall and wide.

Creepy crawlies

The diversity of the creepy crawlies – the flies, scorpions, woodlice and their many relatives – is hard to capture. The Museum holds more than 30 million specimens of these arthropods, gathered over 300 years, and belonging to about 600,000 species – a fraction of the known diversity.

Arthropods are characterised by a jointed body and exoskeleton, and have representatives in every habitat, from spiders on Everest to crabs crawling over sulphurous deep-sea vents and parasitic lice at home in our hair. They come in a bewildering variety of shapes and sizes, with fantastic colours and patterns. Many are armed with impressive weapons, while others create amazing architecture such as the webs of spiders.

All adult arthropods have a hard external skeleton, which performs the same function as a suit of armour. The word arthropod means jointed limb, and the number of limbs is an easy guide to the different groups: insects have six legs, spiders, scorpions and mites have eight, while crustaceans which we are familiar with such as crabs, prawns and lobsters have 10. Centipedes have between 30 and 100 and the millipedes up to 400 – never 1,000.

This diverse group plays an important part in our lives. Some pollinate our food crops or play a big role in soil fertility, while others damage our crops and spread disease. Museum scientists are working all over the world to understand their impact on us – and our impact on them. Our scientists monitor the diversity of

ABOVE The Museum has the oldest and most important entomology collection in the world, containing over 34 million insects and arachnids including, from the top: the birdwing butterfly, the blood-red cymothoe, the blue morpho, the *Milionia paradisea* moth and the blue mountain butterfly.

insects and other arthropods in soil and leaf litter in the UK and around the world, and assess their ecological role. In South America and other parts of the tropics, we are searching for new species of parasitoid wasps that can act as natural control agents of many pest insects, and in China, we study the impact of overgrazing on pollinating bumblebees.

From fleas to flour beetles, arthropods make their homes in our homes. Most are harmless, and a few helpful, but some are destructive and chew through clothing, furniture and roof timbers. At the Museum, too, we have to be on constant alert for them. The collections we look after are a potential paradise for the long-haired larvae of museum beetles, which include the common carpet beetle found in many houses. The larvae feed on natural fibres such as silk, wool, fur, leather and any dried animal remains. When newly hatched, they can crawl through minute cracks in wooden cabinets. We keep our collections in specially-built and temperature controlled environments in which pests cannot breed.

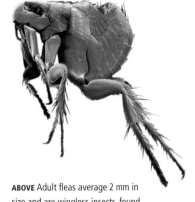

ABOVE Adult fleas average 2 mm in size and are wingless insects, found everywhere except the Arctic. A jumping flea accelerates 50 times faster than a space shuttle.

BELOW Henry Walter Bates (1825–1892) spent 11 years in the Amazon, collected more than 14,000 arthropod specimens and identified 8,000 species. He made detailed notes of everything he collected, and illustrated many of them.

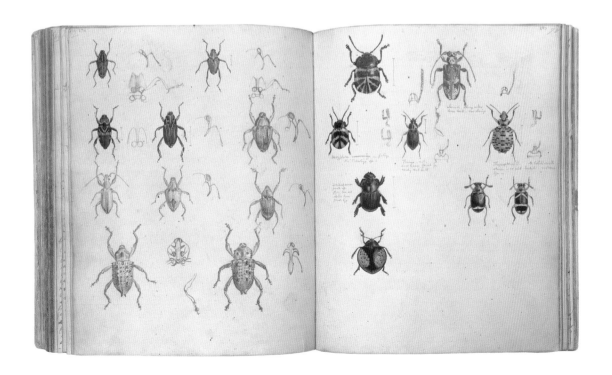

Human evolution

Our evolutionary story is still incomplete and what evidence exists is fragmented and difficult to read. New discoveries deepen our understanding, but a single find can also raise new questions. When the partial skeleton of a small female *Australopithecus afarensis*, was found in Ethiopia in 1974, it captured the world's attention. Named after a Beatles song, Lucy was about 3.2 million years old, had a small brain, long arms and short legs, and the structure of her knee and hip showed that she had routinely walked upright on two legs.

From these first steps, the ancestors of modern humans evolved, as makers of tools, fire and cultures. It was not a simple, orderly progression – at times, several different species of early human relatives co-existed with our ancestors, only to die out. We use the term human to describe all members of the genus *Homo*, from the early small-brained forms and presumed tool-makers, such as *Homo rudolfensis* and *Homo habilis*, to our own species *Homo sapiens*, usually referred to as modern humans.

Museum scientists support the view that *Homo sapiens* evolved in Africa and started to spread across the world from about 100,000 years ago, but that it was not the first human species to spread out of Africa. Who the first migrants were, and what they were like, is one of the hottest debates in human evolution. Most scientists assumed that you needed a big brain and sophisticated tools to be a successful migrant. But, since 1999, five early human skulls

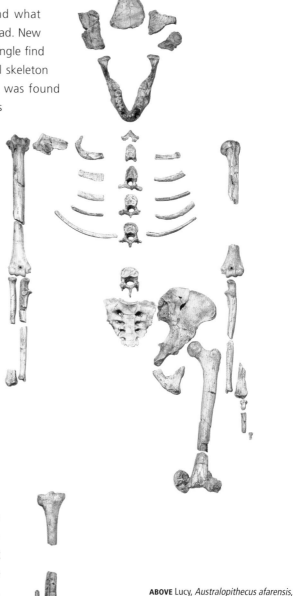

ABOVE Lucy, *Australopithecus afarensis*, is one of the most important fossils ever discovered. She is an early human relative that provided clear evidence of apes that walked upright.

assigned to the species *Homo erectus*, about 1.8 million years old, have been unearthed at Dmanisi, in Georgia. They were hundreds of thousands of years older than anyone expected; their brains were small and they only had simple tools. Arguments continue about their relationship to other early human species.

When modern humans reached Europe about 50,000 years ago, they encountered Neanderthals who had lived across Europe and western Asia from more than 200,000 years ago. Seemingly losing out to the newcomers, the Neanderthals disappear from the fossil record about 40,000 years ago. Recent research, however, suggests that they interbred with our ancestors.

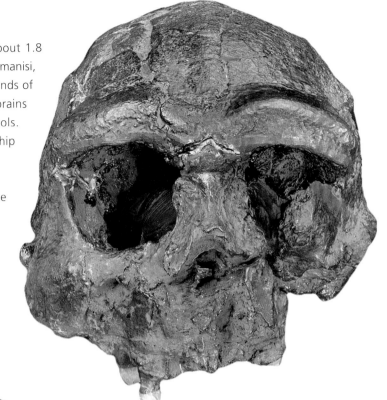

ABOVE *Homo erectus* came on the scene about 1.9 million years ago. They are the oldest known humans to have possessed modern human-like body proportions – longer legs and shorter arms.

LEFT Human evolution has been pieced together from various finds such as this. Discovered in 1921 in Broken Hill, northern Rhodesia (now Kabwe, Zambia), this skull is about 300,000 years old and probably lived at the same time as early *Homo sapiens* in other parts of Africa.

Neanderthals and modern humans are but two of the many branches of the human family tree. Another was discovered on the Indonesian island of Flores in 2003 and described as a new species, *Homo floresiensis,* and in 2013 a large assemblage of fossils assigned to a new species, *Homo naledi*, was discovered in the Rising Star cave system, South Africa. Dated to around 60,000 and 300,000 years ago, respectively, these surprising new species were contemporary with our own, and their late survival and comparatively primitive body shapes are challenging pre-existing ideas of tool use, competition between human species, and the importance of large brains.

Exactly when humans first settled in Britain is a focus for Museum scientists collaborating in a multi-institutional project to understand Britain's first people, their environment and how they lived. The oldest archaeological evidence shows signs of people in the UK about 900,000 years ago, but the oldest fossil human remains are about 500,000 years old, from Boxgrove in West Sussex, England. Bones from horses, deer and rhinos bear the cut-marks of stone tools these people used to butcher the animals. About 100,000 years later, at Swanscombe in Kent, remains of a skull suggest that the evolution of Neanderthals was already underway. They would still be there when the first modern humans arrived in Britain about 42,000 years ago.

LEFT Our species, *Homo sapiens*, originated in Africa, before dispersing around the world and becoming the only surviving species of human left today.

Around 15,000 years ago Britain was still connected to mainland Europe, which meant that early settlers could walk there. One community of Ice Age Britons established themselves in Gough's Cave, Somerset. These people were the Magdalenians, a cultural group of Cro-Magnon hunter-gatherers from southwest Europe who were skilled toolmakers. Gough's Cave has been an important archaeological site since the nineteenth century and, in 1903, a near-complete skeleton known as Cheddar Man was unearthed. This modern human has been dated to around 10,000 years ago.

Museum scientists have found and studied other ~14,700-years-old remains from this site, and signs of cannibalism have been discovered. Very distinct cut marks were found on some human bones and even human tooth marks. Other bones show cut marks where soft tissue has been meticulously removed, and three skulls were carefully shaped to create cups or bowls. And the discovery of a forearm bone with zigzag marks carved into it to create a pattern, suggests that the engraving may have been a way of remembering the deceased's life or death. All these remains suggest that the cannibalistic acts were part of ritualistic cannibalism, and the hunter-gatherers were not eating each other out of necessity.

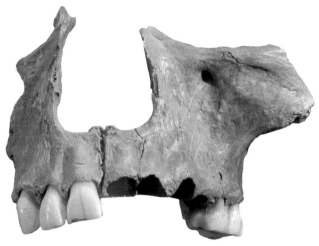

ABOVE Upper jaw of a teenager. Found at Gough's cave, this 14,700-year-old bone is in two parts with cut marks where flesh has been removed.

LEFT One of the human skulls carefully shaped into a cup or bowl by the people who lived at Gough's Cave 14,700 years ago.

Today

1
million years ago

2
million years ago

3
million years ago

4
million years ago

5
million years ago

6
million years ago

7
million years ago

Homo sapiens

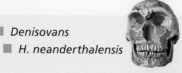
■ *Denisovans*
■ *H. neanderthalensis*

■ *H. daliensis*
■ *H. heidelbergensis*

■ *H. antecessor*

■ *H. erectus*

■ **HUMANS**

■ *Homo rudolfensis*

■ *Homo habilis*

■ *Ardipithecus ramidus*

■ **EARLY HOMININS**

■ *Ardipithecus kadabba*

■ *Orrorin tugenensis*

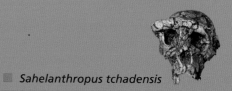
■ *Sahelanthropus tchadensis*

■ *H. floresiensis*   ■ *H. luzonensis*

■ *H. naledi*

■ ROBUST AUSTRALOPITHS

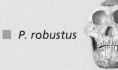

■ *P. robustus*

■ *P. boisei*

■ *Au. sediba*

■ *Au. africanus*   ■ *Au. garhi*

■ *Paranthropus aethiopicus*

■ AUSTRALOPITHS

■ *Kenyanthropus platyops*   ■ *Au. bahrelghazali*   ■ *Au. afarensis*   ■ *Au. deyiremeda*

■ *Australopithecus anamensis*

The earliest known hominin species are nearly 7 million years old. Modern humans are now the only surviving hominin species, but until recently we coexisted with other hominin species.

Lasting impressions

Some specimens capture a lifetime's growth, the growth happening at very different paces. A patch of lichen on a rock may expand no more than a millimetre in 50 years. A bamboo might extend more than 20 metres in a single two-month growing season. Some specimens on the other hand record a single event. A thin red line running through a coral captures the sudden pollution of its environment with iron. Ripples in sand, frozen into rock, are marked with what are possibly the footprints of a primitive reptile that walked across a sandy beach, 230 million years ago.

Many specimens show growth rings, marking cycles of growth over months and years. In a fossil tree trunk they have turned to rock as the wood has been replaced by minerals. There are also growth patterns

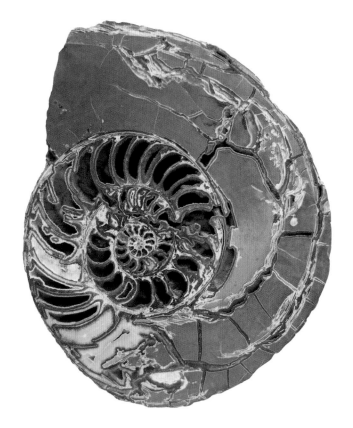

ABOVE Bamboo is the fastest growing plant in the world, and giant bamboos are the largest member of the grass family.

LEFT Spiral-shaped true ammonites were common in the oceans between 66 and 200 million years ago.

LEFT Formed in the Tyneside coal mine during the 1800s this rock is a stark reminder of the dusty underground mining conditions that many endured.

BELOW LEFT Agate is a microcrystalline quartz made up of twisted crystal fibres which make it hard and durable. It commonly forms in fractures across or between volcanic lava flows.

BELOW Folded gneiss is a common metamorphic rock formed from sedimentary rocks that experience intense heat and high pressures deep within the Earth. This process squashes the layers of rock producing the patterns seen here.

in goat horns and seashells. A beautiful fossil of an ammonite, an extinct relative of the octopus and squid, illustrates how it grew by adding chambers to its coiled shell. After death, the chambers became mineralised and filled with crystals.

And remarkably, the delicate slice of Sunday stone records cycles too – of the working rhythm of a coalmine in the 1880s. Layers of white barium sulphate crystals were deposited from water flowing over the rocks, remaining white on Sundays and public holidays when the mine was closed, but turning dark on those working days when coal dust washed out of the mine, creating a musical score in black and cream.

Earth Hall

Earth has produced spectacular species, both above and below the ground in its 4,540-million-year history. For many, the best-known land-living species celebrated by the Museum are the dinosaurs, and one of the most spectacular recent additions to the collection is a near complete *Stegosaurus* (see pp.28–29). This specimen was found in Wyoming, USA with more than 90 per cent of its bones intact, making it the most complete *Stegosaurus* fossil skeleton ever found.

But there are treasures below the surface, too. Fluorite and willemite specimens glow under UV light. Rainbow-coloured opal and glittering fool's gold – also known as pyrite – also catch the eye. A trio of salt-petre (potassium nitrate), sulphur and charcoal have explosive results – they form gunpowder when combined – and a fossil of the extinct plant, a lepidodendron tree, may look diminutive enough but it drove the industrial revolution as one of the main components of the fossil fuel coal. There are devil's toenails, the shell of an extinct mollusc and a perfectly preserved stingray from 50 million years ago.

TOP The mineral sulphur plays a part in most of Earth's biochemical processes.

ABOVE Azurite is a soft, deep blue copper mineral very similar chemically to the green mineral malachite.

BELOW The devil's toenail is the common name for the claw-like fossil shells of an extinct genus of oyster, *Gryphaea*.

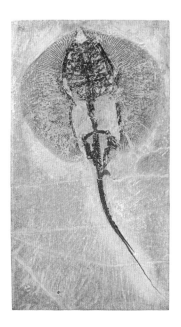

ABOVE The finely preserved fossil of this male freshwater stingray was found in mudstone that was part of the floor of a deep lake covering a large part of Wyoming, USA 50 million years ago.

LEFT A section of orbicular diorite showing spheres of different minerals crystallised around tiny cores. The rock crystallised from molten magma, but exactly how is unknown. Cut and polished, the rock makes a striking building stone.

Minerals

A mineral is a naturally occurring substance formed through geological processes. Each has a unique chemical composition and crystal structure. Two minerals can have the same chemical elements but form quite different crystals – diamond and graphite, for example, are both crystalline carbon, but have radically different structures and properties. Rocks are made up of one or more minerals, or fragments of other rocks.

The Museum's remarkable collection of minerals and rocks represents Earth's geodiversity and its range of geological components. The collection is especially strong in material from the UK and Europe and former British territories and colonies. There are nearly 350 items that can be identified from Sir Hans Sloane's original founding collections, including ornamental boxes and drawers of minerals once used as medicines.

Two major collections are kept as distinct entities: the Sir Arthur Russell Collection of British Minerals and the Ashcroft Swiss Collection. Sir Arthur Russell was a famous collector of British minerals who left more than 12,500 specimens to the Museum. They include rare samples collected from sites no longer in existence or now inaccessible, such as the closed copper and tin mines of Cornwall in southern England. Frederick Noel Ashcroft's collection of Swiss minerals must be amongst

ABOVE This 717-gramme Latrobe gold nugget from Australia still has its individual crystals intact. Since gold is soft and erodes easily, a nugget preserving its crystalline structure like this is a very rare find.

FAR LEFT Malachite, which contains copper has been used as a decorative material and as a source of copper metal for millennia, its minute crystals often grow together forming beautiful radial patterns, which when sliced are very attractive.

LEFT Jasper is a variety of quartz with microscopic impurities that give it a variety of colours in hues of red, orange, brown and black. With unique growth patterns, it is very popular in jewellery and for ornaments.

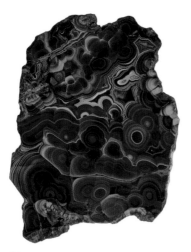

The Vault

Minerals are also prized for their great beauty, or their historical and cultural stories. Diamonds, sapphires (like this padparadscha), emeralds and rubies are all rich sources of these tales. The Aurora Pyramid of Hope is a world-class celebration of naturally coloured diamonds. Unlike the white diamonds, these 296 stones, together weighing 267 carats, represents much of the colour spectrum. The colour of diamond is caused by minute amounts of trace elements or structural defects that affect the way light is reflected and absorbed. When seen under ultraviolet light, many of these stones fluoresce a different colour.

the world's best-curated collection. He recorded meticulously the locality of each of the 7,000 specimens, and also kept an extensive photographic record.

Not all minerals start in the ground. Some come from the sky in the form of meteorites. Some of the most fantastic of these are cared for in the collection, 4,933 in total. Meteorites are fragments of rock that have been knocked off planetary bodies and eventually fall to Earth. Most come from asteroids, but some rare specimens have been linked to the Moon and Mars. A few are rich in water, sulphur and organic (carbon-rich) compounds – materials that may have provided the chemical building blocks for life on Earth.

Meteorites offer an opportunity to study extraterrestrial material, which would otherwise require sample-return space missions. Meteorite research covers many wide-ranging questions from the origin and evolution of our Solar System, to the process of impact cratering, to the potential habitability of other planets.

BELOW At 4.5 billion years old, this sparkling Imilac meteorite dates back to the beginning of our solar system. It is a slice of an ancient pallasite meteorite formed in the asteroid belt, located between Mars and Jupiter.

Earth's treasury

Natural mineral crystals are often very beautiful, like tiny architectural masterpieces. We cut and shape some further as gemstones to enhance their aesthetic and bring out their vivid colours. The important collection kept at the Museum includes the most valued of these, the rubies, sapphires and emeralds, as well as historic diamond specimens that date back to the first discoveries in South Africa. Other beautiful gemstones, such as fluorite in many colours, may be too soft or fragile to be worn, but are sought after by collectors.

We might place a high value on precious gems and metals, but each mineral and rock has its own special properties, and its own value to us. Dark haematite is the main source of the metal iron. Salt (sodium chloride) flavours our food. Granite is a superbly tough building stone, limestone is more easily carved. Titanium dioxide is the key ingredient in white paint, china clay makes fine porcelain. The rare metal platinum is used not only in jewellery, but also in catalytic converters to remove harmful gases from exhaust fumes. Silica, the

BELOW To create glittering gemstones, minerals are cut in ways to enhance their aesthetic qualities and colours like these in the Museum's collections; from left: aquamarine, star ruby, tourmaline, topaz, yellow sapphire, water tourmaline, peridot, star sapphire and morganite.

commonest rock-forming compound on Earth, has become one of the most important to our lives today. Among many uses, it is the basic ingredient for the glass in our windows, and the raw material for the chips that run our computers.

Diamond has value beyond its worth as a gem. It is not only the hardest natural material known, but uniquely combines this with other properties; for example, it can survive pressures that destroy most other minerals. This is put to use in a 'diamond anvil', a device that generates extreme pressures by applying a moderate force over a tiny area – the tip of a diamond. Squeezing other minerals between two diamond points allows scientists to study how the minerals would behave under the kinds of pressures found below the surface, deep in Earth's mantle.

One of the world's most common minerals, quartz, is natural silica and is prized both as ornamental stones and gems. It is found in nearly every geological environment and as part of almost every rock type. It comes in a bewildering variety of colours and shapes, from fine single crystals of purple amethyst and clear rock crystal to gloriously patterned masses of microscopic crystals in agate.

From the beginning

Earth may be 4,540 million years old, but its story begins even earlier with the origins of the universe itself. Most scientists believe about 15,000 million years ago, all matter – and time – came into being in the big bang, when a tiny fireball of infinite density and heat exploded, and expanded, perhaps even faster than the speed of light. Matter gradually clumped together to form galaxies and stars. Our own galaxy evolved about 10,000 million years ago, our solar system formed about 4,567 million years ago after which Earth slowly took its present shape.

ABOVE This rare fossilised flower of *Porana oeningensis* is about 20 million years old, preserved as a thin film of carbon and discovered in Germany.

The earliest signs of single-celled life come from sedimentary rocks 4,000 million years old, and rocks containing what many regard as the oldest known fossils (c. 3,500 million years old) are in the Museum collection. More complex forms did not emerge until about 550 million years ago. It seems there was then an explosion of life, with many bizarre creatures evolving that bear no resemblance to anything living today, and others that are still remarkably familiar in form. The 500-million-year-old marine predator *Anomalocaris* was pieced together from fossilised remains, each originally thought to be a separate animal. We have found 570-million-year-old fossils of jellyfish that look very like they do today.

BELOW By studying a single bone of this creature and meticulously comparing it to the bones of other species, Richard Owen, in 1839, correctly predicted that it belonged to a giant extinct bird that could not fly – the moa from New Zealand.

Plants and animals populated the dry land between about 470 and 395 million years ago. Invertebrates, such as crawling insects and giant centipedes, were the first to emerge, and four-legged vertebrates, such as slow-moving amphibians, followed quickly. There were sprawling amphibians and massive reptiles such as the bulky *Bradysaurus* – its limbs more like crudely hewn boulders – and eventually, the dinosaurs.

BIG BANG

SOLAR SYSTEM BORN
EARTH FORMS
MOON FORMS

OLDEST ROCKS

FIRST RIVERS, LAKES & SEA

15000   13500   5000   4567 4540 4533   4030   3850

The first large-scale geological map

Earth's geology has also changed and being able to date rock formations is vital in geological research. Among the Museum's many treasures are maps made by William 'Strata' Smith (1769–1839). Known as the father of English geology, he produced the first large-scale geological map in the world. Smith was a canal engineer and, as he was cutting through rock, noticed that the fossils were always found in a certain order from bottom to top, and that the same order appeared at locations elsewhere. He reasoned that fossils could be used to match and date geological formations wherever they were found. This principle is still used.

The fossil record appears to show that life on Earth has gone through cycles of extinction, when whole groups disappear from the fossil record, and other groups then diversify to take their place. The best known of these is the event that caused the extinction of the non-avian dinosaurs. But there have been five such cycles. Our species may be causing a sixth. We emerged against the backdrop of the great cycles of freezing and warming we call the ice ages. Somehow, we learned to survive and prosper. Many of the great beasts that evolved alongside us during these periods are now extinct, some possibly at our hands. Today, our success continues to threaten the survival of the creatures with which we share our environment.

BELOW Trilobites thrived in the shallow oceans in prehistoric times. Scientists think this group piled up together to spawn and suffocated. This mating behaviour is exactly the same as their living relative, the horseshoe crab.

3460   SIMPLE CELLS

3000

1000

542 EXPLOSION OF MARINE LIFE

470 LAND PLANTS
410 INSECTS
395 ANIMALS MOVE ONTO LAND

360 AMPHIBIANS

320 TROPICAL RAINFORESTS
315 FLYING INSECTS
   REPTILES

225 MAMMALS

147 BIRDS
140 FLOWERING PLANTS

66 DINOSAURS WIPED OUT
45 HIMALAYAS FORMED
15 ANCESTORS OF GREAT APES
0.2 MODERN HUMANS
   PRESENT DAY

Volcanoes and earthquakes

Powerful forces at work deep within Earth have shaped its surface, and volcanoes and earthquakes are the visible evidence of these forces. Volcanoes cause devastation when they erupt, as the Earth's crust is thrown into convulsions and explosive eruptions fire molten rock and ash high into the air, while lava flows and pyroclastic flows of lava and ash can wipe out everything in their path. Earthquakes wreak destruction directly or by causing tsunamis or landslides. Water heated by underground magma can transport metals and other elements in solution and deposit them as minerals in rocks nearer the surface. Volcanologists investigate this magma, wearing special suits that can withstand temperatures up to 900°C. These efforts reveal more about Earth's processes and help us better understand our planet.

There is significant human cost to the planet's violent motion. In human history, the eruption of Mount Vesuvius in Italy, on the morning of 24 August, AD 79, was among the most devastating, catching the population of Pompeii unawares, evidenced by people and animals found entombed in ash. The 1995 earthquake in Kobe, Japan, also caused massive damage and loss of life and, since then, there has been even greater destruction. In December 2004, an earthquake deep below the Indian Ocean unleashed a tsunami that killed more than 200,000 people and wrecked coastlines from Sumatra to India. In March 2011, Japan's most powerful earthquake since records began struck the northeast

TOP When lava cools extremely quickly it forms this smooth volcanic glass, called obsidian. When sliced, obsidian is very sharp and has been used to make cutting blades for thousands of years.

ABOVE Naturally occurring sulphur is yellow. It is commonly associated with hot springs and volcanic craters, where it forms from a toxic cocktail of gases and water vapour given off by fumarolic vents.

LEFT The beautiful patterns in this folded schist rock formed as layers of mudstones were subjected to very high pressures and temperatures.

coast, triggering a massive tsunami which then led to a nuclear crisis and huge leaks of radiation. In April 2015, a powerful earthquake on the morning of 25 April killed 9,000 people in Nepal.

Devastating as they are, volcanoes and earthquakes are only minor surface signs of far greater forces at work deep below, forces so massive that whole continents are moved across the planet's surface as part of giant tectonic plates. These plates are in constant, slow motion. At their margins, new plate forms or sinks slowly back into the depths. It is along these lines of weakness that most volcanoes and earthquakes occur. The drifting plates are driven by giant currents of rock that flow through Earth's mantle, the 2,900-kilometre zone between the plate and the molten outer core. Over geological time their movement throws up mountains and creates new oceans.

Deep-sea exploration in the 1960s revealed vast mountain ranges beneath the oceans, marking plate boundaries where new plates are created. There, hot mineral-laden water escapes from chimney-like openings called hydrothermal vents. An extraordinary range of life thrives in this dark hostile environment. Discovery of this world helped our Museum geologists and their Russian colleagues, searching for new mineral deposits, to understand some puzzling fossil layers they had found in the Ural Mountains of central Russia. They realised that they were looking at an ancient deep-sea floor, about 370 million years old.

ABOVE These giant tubeworms are 2 metres tall and they can take 200 years to reach this size. They thrive in the hydrothermal vents at plate boundaries on the ocean floor together with clams and crustaceans.

BELOW Flows of burning lava from a volcanic eruption can reach 1,250°C or more, burning everything in their path.

Restless surface

Changes to Earth's surface may come suddenly, with a violent landslide or raging storm, or slowly, drip by drip, over millions of years. Ours is a restless planet, and change is part of its nature. Wind, water, ice and gravity sculpt the landscape, wearing down mountains and carving out deep ravines. Their destructive power is matched only by their power to build, as they carry millions of tonnes of debris that will in time settle and cement to form new rocks and new landscapes.

The smooth texture of a rounded pebble tells of its long journey along a river, tumbling and rolling in water, while a jagged fragment may have been trapped in the ice of a flowing glacier, with no opportunity to rub against its companions. The stripes of a lake bed sediment show the annual rhythm of debris flushed into the lake with spring floods.

Water is the greatest shaper of the world's landscapes. It wears away at the surface both chemically and physically. As ice it can crack open boulders and grind out deep valleys. As flowing water it can

BELOW The Seven Sisters cliffs, in the Seven Sisters Country Park on England's southeast coast, are an extraordinary example of chalk, a soft white, very finely grained pure limestone that has built up gradually over millions of years.

A journey in rock

This mineralised limestone, with its complex fragments of layered pink crystals among grey debris, tells of a long cycle of change. First, a cave formed as groundwater eroded the rock, then minerals grew in brightly coloured layers on its roof and walls. An earthquake caused the roof to collapse, and water crept between the broken debris, depositing new mineral crystals.

eat away caves and build up towering stalagmites, where watery sediments begin to turn to rock as they are compacted. It can sweep up fragments of rock and carry them hundreds of kilometres, then deposit them in vast sandbanks and river deltas.

Life is also part of the restless process of change. Limestone hills and chalk cliffs are formed from the remains of living things. Over the millennia, billions of skeletons of tiny marine creatures sank to the bottom of the sea, building layers hundreds of metres deep. In time, these were compressed and cemented together, and gradually land movements and changing sea levels exposed them at the surface. These carbon-rich rocks are part of the planet's carbon cycle, which circulates carbon between living and non-living worlds, and between the surface and deep mantle.

BELOW LEFT Fossil ripple marks preserved in sandstone. The detailed structure of the ripple marks can reveal a lot about past sedimentary environments.

BELOW Deep grooves in this glacially striated and polished rock are the marks of other rock fragments frozen into the moving ice of a glacier, and gouging like a chisel across the rock surface.

Images of nature

Before the arrival of photography and film, scientists depended on artists to produce detailed illustrations. The best were acclaimed for the accuracy of their work and were highly sought after. They also provided evidence of new species from far-flung lands and were sources of valuable scientific information. Contemporary scientists still illustrate their own work, but drawing now sits alongside a suite of technological methods for recording nature, from scanning electron microscopes to satellites.

The Museum holds irreplaceable historic prints, watercolours and paintings spanning more than 350 years as well as modern artworks, including images created by Museum scientists, imaging specialists and photographers. Beautiful and intriguing, these works are an important visual record of the natural world over time.

Of the many arresting depictions is a haunting chalk drawing of a giant tortoise by Bryan Kneale from 1986, and a seventeenth-century oil painting of a dodo, attributed to the Flemish artist Roelandt Savery. There are more modern interpretations of the dodo, too, one in acrylic by artist and Museum scientist Dr Julian Pender Hume.

BELOW LEFT Bryan Kneale produced a series of these bone drawings from specimens in the Museum collections while he was teaching at the Royal College of Art.

BELOW John Fleming, a surgeon in the East India Co. amassed more than 1,000 botanical illustrations including this Indian water lily, *Nymphaea rubra*.

Wildlife Photographer of the Year

LEFT Flashy fighters by Hitesh Oberoi. In the hills of southern Maharashtra, India, two male Deccan fan-throated lizards side up as a prelude to a fight, displaying their dazzling colours like battle flags. From the 2021 Wildlife Photographer of the Year competition.

BELOW Lockdown chicks by Gagana Mendis Wickramasinghe. In the spring of 2020, three rose-ringed parakeet chicks pop their heads out of a nesting hole as their father returns with food. Watching was 10-year-old Gagana on the balcony of his parents' bedroom, in Colombo, Sir Lanka. From the 2021 Wildlife Photographer of the Year competition.

Every autumn, we host one of our most popular exhibitions, Wildlife Photographer of the Year, showcasing winning entries from the annual competition. This is the largest and most prestigious wildlife photographic contest in the world and receives more than 45,000 entries each year. The competition is open to both amateur enthusiasts and established professionals, while the special junior section seeks to encourage and nurture the next generation of aspiring nature photographers.

The exhibition of the award-winners aims to inspire wonder in the splendour and variety of life on Earth through its inspirational photographs. From plant portraits to wildlife in danger, the striking images capture the wild beauty of our planet and remind us of its fragility. The exhibition tours the UK and three continents, enabling millions of people to absorb the beauty and majesty of the world.

Among the categories is a portfolio award for young photographers aged 18 to 25 and a wildlife photojournalism award. The overall junior winner is awarded a prize of £1,000, and the winner of the ultimate accolade, Wildlife Photographer of the Year, a prize of £10,000.

Wildlife Garden

Opened in July 1995 the Wildlife Garden is the Museum's first living exhibition of the countryside. It was designed and planted to illustrate a range of British semi-natural habitats including meadow, chalk downland, ponds, woodland, hedgerow and heathland. Volunteers play an important part in its upkeep and help with planting, pruning, composting and coppicing, and they and Museum staff contribute to the Museum's long-term study of flora and fauna within the garden.

BELOW The map shows all the different habitats that have been created to attract a variety of wildlife in an urban environment.

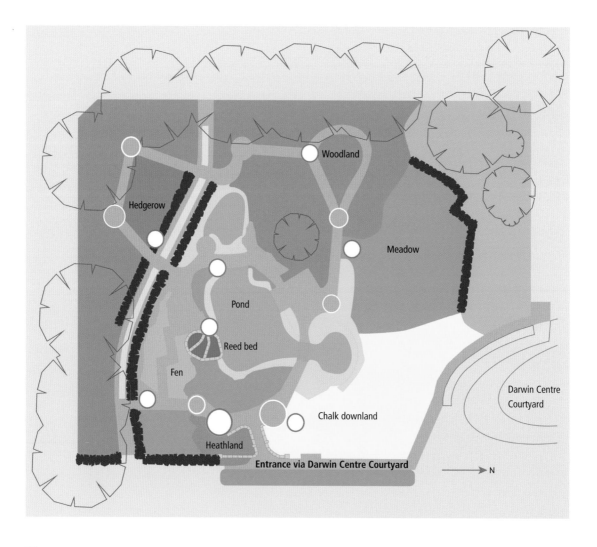

Woodland

Hedgerow

Meadow

Pond

Reed bed

Fen

Darwin Centre Courtyard

Chalk downland

Heathland

Entrance via Darwin Centre Courtyard

N

Despite its position alongside one of London's busiest roads, the garden's wildlife has thrived, and a surprising number of species have been recorded foraging and nesting. While frogs, toads and newts were introduced deliberately, other animals came in of their own accord. Blackbirds, wrens, robins, finches, tits and blackcaps enjoy the habitats to nest in and feed from, and many birds use the garden as a seasonal stopover. On summer evenings pipistrelle bats pursue mosquitoes and other small insects. More than 350 beetle species and more than 550 species of moth and butterfly have been recorded.

In spring some birds, such as long-tailed tits, prepare to nest as early as February. Later, primroses, bluebells and wild garlic bloom in the woodland, and frogs, toads and newts mate in the ponds. By summer, moorhens are feeding their young, while dragonflies and damselflies hunt over the water and habitats. The chalk downland area is a mass of flowers, including wild marjoram, lady's bedstraw and orchids. Autumn brings toadstools, and more than 150 species of fungi have been recorded. Visiting birds, such as redwing, fly in to feed on the bright berries. In winter the garden seems still, but beneath the fallen leaves life continues and before long spring plants start producing their first foliage.

ABOVE The Jersey tiger moth is a colourful arrival in the garden, its main flight period is July to September. It flies both in the daytime and at night.

BELOW LEFT The Wildlife Garden is an urban oasis, home to many plant and animal species that are monitored by the Museum's scientists and studied by school groups.

BELOW With its bright red breast the European robin is a common sight in the Museum's garden throughout the year.

The Natural History Museum at Tring

The Natural History Museum has a sister museum in the Hertfordshire town of Tring, a charming Victorian treasure trove 40 minutes by train from London. Tring was the family seat of the Rothschilds, a rich banking family, and this delightful museum began as a twenty-first birthday present to Lionel Walter, son of the First Baron Rothschild. From two cottages in the grounds, it rapidly expanded to fit his growing natural history collections.

ABOVE The endangered St Vincent parrot, *Amazona guildingii*, is found only on the Caribbean island of St Vincent.

LEFT The eccentric Lord Rothschild hitched zebras to his carriage and rode on a giant tortoise. He also kept many live animals, including several cassowaries.

BELOW Over 2,000 years ago, an ancient Egyptian painstakingly wrapped and embalmed this domestic cat as a religious offering to an animal-headed god. This specimen was bought by two sisters in 1914, who donated it to the Museum.

By the time of his death in 1937, Rothschild had accumulated the largest collection of animal specimens assembled by one person. He left the buildings and land to the Natural History Museum, along with hundreds of thousands of specimens, including both the public displays and the scientific research collections, and a library of 30,000 books. It was one of the most important gifts in the Museum's history. Visiting Tring today is like stepping back in time. The six galleries are much as Rothschild left them, crowded with specimens from floor to ceiling. Flocks of birds adorn the walls – from the everyday to the exotic, birds of prey and colourful parrots. On the upper floors, elephants, rhinos and a camel parade along the tops of cases, while sharks hang overhead and fish swim down the walls.

Darwin's finches

Some of the most famous specimens in the bird collection are the finches from the Galapagos Islands, which were collected by Charles Darwin and others on the *Beagle* voyage in the 1830s. The specimens, which include this common cactus-finch, *Geospiza scandens*, are known as Darwin's finches. They are now seen as an iconic example of evolution by natural selection, their beaks adapted over time to feed on different sorts of foods. However, Darwin did not recognise their importance at first – in fact he learned more from breeding pigeons back home in England. Seeing how new varieties could be created by selective breeding helped him to realise the power of natural selection in shaping new kinds of living things.

Smaller treasures hide behind wooden doors – dressed fleas and huge stick insects. There are atmospheric displays of more than 700 kangaroos, ostriches, snakes, domestic dogs and champion greyhounds, or wonders such as the platypus, the star-nosed mole and the extinct Tasmanian wolf. Among the many faces peering out are some of Rothschild's favourite species, among them the brightly coloured cassowaries and Aldabra giant tortoises. As well as having the permanent galleries, the Museum puts on three temporary exhibitions a year, on topics as diverse as parasites and animal mummies.

The Natural History Museum's bird collection was transferred to Tring in the 1970s, where it is now kept in environmentally controlled conditions. Approaching one and a half million specimens, including around 300,000 sets of eggs, the collection represents 95 per cent of all known living bird species. Under the care of the Bird Group, this is one of our most actively researched collections, and hundreds of visitors come every year to study there.

OVERLEAF A tray of the Museum's vast weevil collection. Characterised by their long snouts or rostra, there are more than 65,000 described species.

BELOW Some animals at the Museum at Tring are hybrids, like this hybrid of a puma and a leopard. Walter liked animals that were unusual or rare and collected them.

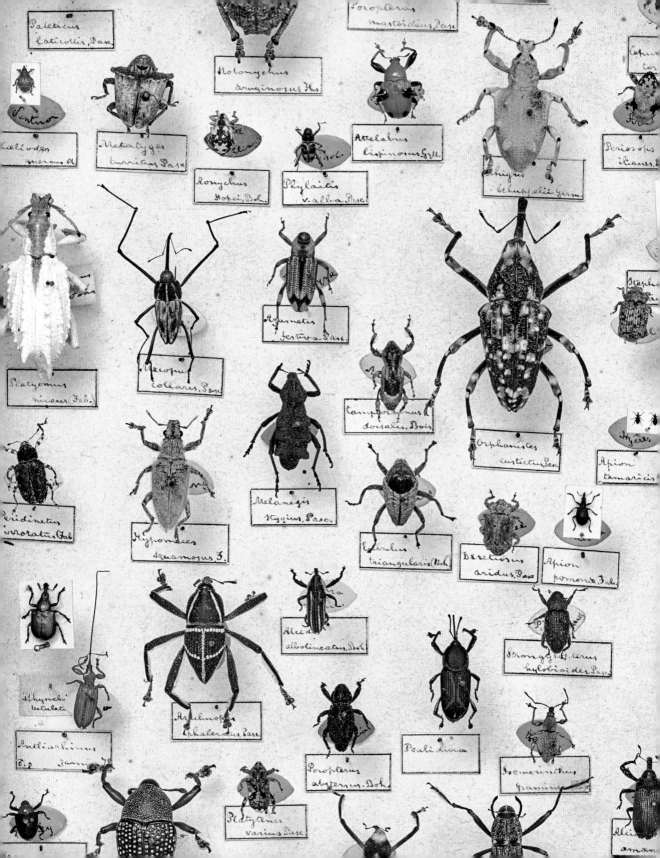

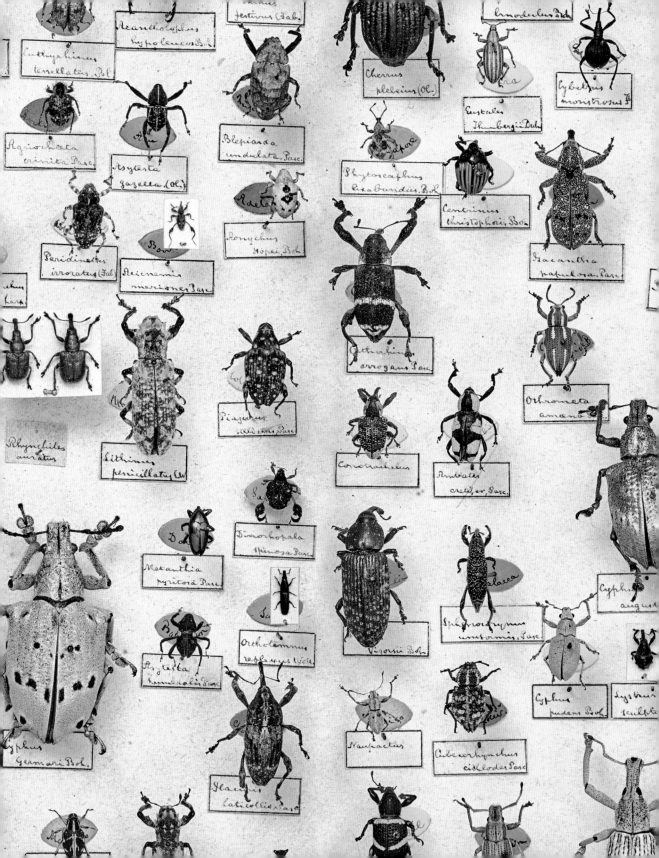

Our science

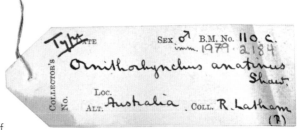

The Natural History Museum's collections have grown steadily over the years, and now number more than 80 million objects. Together they represent virtually all groups of plants and animals, past and present, plus the rocks and minerals that make up our planet. Over one million books, journals, manuscripts, maps and half a million artworks are a further treasure trove of knowledge. There are specimens collected 400 years ago, and eighteenth-century paintings recording creatures no European had ever seen before such as the platypus and the hippopotamus. There are fossils of single-celled organisms from the beginnings of life on Earth and meteorites made of material as old as the solar system. Together, they are an unrivalled database of our planet's past and a resource to help conserve its future.

ABOVE Each of the specimens in the Museum's collections is labelled to say where and when it was collected. Scientists need these details to study and compare specimens.

BELOW Painted in China *c.*1812–1824 this exquisite watercolour of a male lesser bird of paradise, *Paradisaea minor*, was commissioned by John Reeves, a tea inspector for the East India Company and a keen amateur naturalist.

The art of collecting began in the 1700s, when it was fashionable to gather curious objects such as unusual shells or fine mineral crystals. Explorers returning from all corners of the world brought back natural objects to eager private collectors. Discoveries built up as European empires expanded, and collecting became more systematic and organised. As well as finding economically useful products, scientists took interest and wanted to build a catalogue of Earth's diversity, a record of the beauty and strangeness of nature.

Collections were increasingly used as a tool for science, a means of understanding the natural world. From the 1860s, collections were used to show how life on Earth had changed over time, and how species were related, for example how our own species is related to other apes. Collections also became evidence for the theory of evolution. It became important to collect not just one specimen of a species but many, to capture the full range of variation and enable us to determine what species truly exist.

The diversity of the collections is vast. A specimen can be anything from mounted skins to pieces of bone, teeth, hand-sized samples of rock and minerals or those you need a crane to move. Some are more unusual, such as handbags made of crocodile skin, beetles turned into jewels and shells engraved with prayers. There are also slides of tissue and frozen samples of DNA. Even sounds can be specimens. The more we know about each of these objects, the more scientifically valuable they become, bringing the specimen to life and fuelling our scientific work.

Among these treasures are some that are particularly prized, known as types. They are the individual objects that act forever as the dictionary definition of individual species, often the first specimen of that species discovered. Anyone researching a species, or trying to separate out a new one, must refer back to its type. The Museum holds nearly half, 850,000, of the world's type specimens, and some are not what you might expect – the 1901 African okapi type specimen for instance is a belt made from hide from its striped hindquarters. Sometimes, when nothing remains at all, the type is a written description of a species or even an artwork.

The core of the Museum's work is to identify, name and classify species. Each is given a unique scientific name, so researchers across the world using different languages can refer to it without confusion. This has two parts: the genus (a small group of close relatives) followed by the unique species name. Our genus is *Homo* and our species is *sapiens*. Species and genera are grouped again within larger categories to express wider relationships. Lions, *Panthera leo*, and leopards, *Panthera pardus*, are grouped with other cats, the cats with dogs and other carnivores. These in turn are classified as mammals, and so on.

The Museum is also a world-class research centre, with experts on subjects as diverse as snails and space working to uncover the secrets of the unique collections it holds. These collections grow by an average of 150,000 new specimens each year and our loans to other institutions comprise more than 57,000 specimens. It's a global initiative, with collaborators in 70 countries across the world and

ABOVE This belt made from the hide of an okapi is the type specimen of this species.

BELOW Spirit is the common name for industrial alcohol (methylated spirits). It keeps specimens in good condition for a long time, and is especially good for soft-bodied specimens such as whole fish and snakes. Despite extensive research no-one has found anything better at an affordable price.

10,000 visiting researchers. The plants and insects are dry specimens, but many of the zoological objects are kept in spirit, the common name for industrial alcohol (methylated spirits). Spirit keeps specimens in good condition for a long time and is especially good for soft-bodied specimens such as whole fishes and snakes. Despite extensive research, no one has found anything better at an affordable price. Apart from pubs, the Darwin Centre is one of the few buildings in London to have alcohol on tap.

The knowledge our scientists generate can help meet real-life challenges: developing new resources and using existing ones more wisely and protecting our health and our environment. They work globally to understand diseases that affect humans. Studies of parasites, and the vectors that transmit them, lead us to work on a diversity of tropical diseases and find a means to eliminate them. Examples include schistosomiasis, which accounts for 300,000 deaths annually, and soil-transmitted helminths, which infect 1.5 billion people globally. Using new techniques such as molecular biology, researchers extract vital information such as DNA from even the tiniest fragments of a specimen. By examining an organism's unique DNA sequence, scientists can distinguish species that look very similar, such as many mosquitoes. Only some of the 3,500 species of mosquito carry the malaria parasite, which is responsible for three million deaths worldwide each year. Targeting the mosquitoes that carry the parasite is one way of reducing these deaths. But different species need different control methods. DNA sequencing can swiftly distinguish species so we can select the best method for controlling the mosquitoes and so slow the spread of malaria.

Our mineralogists are investigating how minerals behave in the soil to track and minimise the spread of pollution from mines or waste dumps. And in the mountains of Central America, data from satellite images combined with data from vegetation surveys can help foresters to manage and conserve tropical forests. From mountains to the sea, scientists from the Earth Sciences

ABOVE By studying the DNA of organisms that look very similar, such as mosquitoes, scientists can identify those that carry the parasite responsible for malaria such as this mosquito, *Anopheles labanchiae*.

BELOW Some fossils reveal incredible detail, such as this 6–8 million-year-old frog from Spain, *Rana pueyoi*. You can see its skeleton as well as the preserved outline of its body.

department are studying fossil corals from many time periods and regions to better understand how ancient reef systems responded to various types of environmental change. This will help predict how threatened reef systems today might respond to ongoing and future environmental changes. And zoologists are studying nematodes (or roundworms) from fished and pristine seamounts in the Indian Ocean to assess the impact of commercial fishing and other human activities such as mining by determining the factors that are important to the diversity and abundance of nematode species on the seamounts.

Museum scientists are making important discoveries about our planet, its present diversity and the processes generating that diversity. Our botanists, for example, are documenting the plant diversity of islands in the Atlantic and using these 'natural laboratories' to understand plant evolution. In Russia, they are examining the microscopic life of Lake Baikal, the world's largest and deepest lake, to understand how life has adapted and evolved in this unique, isolated environment. Palaeontologists are investigating the early occupation of Britain by humans going back some 900,000 years, and volcanologists are using the information locked in volcanic rocks to learn what is happening inside active volcanoes before they erupt. From deep in the Earth's interior to space the Museum is exploring new analytical techniques to narrow down where our water came from and what happened to it along the way by studying rare meteorites and samples from Apollo missions.

These endeavours are not powered by scientists alone; the public make invaluable contributions to data collection. One of our recent projects is the Big Seaweed Search, encouraging the public to survey the shoreline so scientists can learn about the abundance of seaweed species and how this may change over time in relation to key environmental issues such as rising sea temperature, ocean acidification and non-native species. From gardeners to forensic scientists, our staff deal with more than 10,000 enquiries each year from the public and organisations that need specimens identified through the Angela Marmont Centre. New discoveries are made all the time, either through previously undetected species in an old collection or via new techniques such as DNA analysis or CT scanning.

ABOVE A specimen of the predatory snipe fly captured in Baltic amber, thought to be approximately 35 million years old.

OPPOSITE These mounted seaweeds, the handiwork of women living in Jersey during the 1850s and 1860s, are a charming souvenir from the beach. The delicate sprays of plants are painstakingly flattened out on to postcard-sized pieces of card, which together fold neatly up into a little booklet.

Griffithsia secundiflora.

Laminaria Phyllitis.

Ceramium strictum.

Ulva latissima.

Delesseria sanguinea.

Padina Pavonia.

Griffithsia setacea.

Enteromorpha.

Plocamium coccineum.

Support us....

The Museum is an exempt charity and relies upon the outstanding generosity of our supporters. Continued funding is crucial if we are to maintain our world-class scientific collections, offer inspirational exhibitions and provide innovative opportunities to understand more about our planet.

There are many ways you can support our work, including making a donation of any size, becoming a Member (see below) or Patron, or remembering the Museum with a gift in your Will. To support us, or for more information, please visit our website – nhm.ac.uk/support-us.

Become a Member

Museum Members receive a range of great benefits including free exhibition entry, special events and private views, discounts and priority queueing and exclusive access to the Anning Rooms. Become a Member and help us continue our pioneering research, education and conservation work.

Visit our shops

You can find fantastic gifts and souvenirs for all ages, from young palaeontologists to those looking for exclusive homewares and prints. Our products are inspired by, and support, the Museum's collections and research, with many of them developed in collaboration with our scientists.

Eat and drink

All our eateries are family friendly and have tasty freshly prepared food, including vegetarian, gluten friendly and dairy free products. Our coffee is award winning and all our teas are loose leafed. We have a dedicated children's menu, activity packs and lunch boxes available throughout the Museum.

Shop online

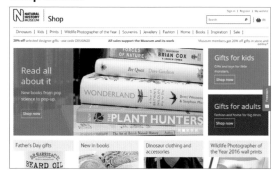

Our online shop has thousands of gifts, from fun, educational toys approved by the Museum's scientists to eclectic homeware. We ship globally. Sign up to our marketing emails and receive 10% off of your first purchase.

Hire the Museum

The Natural History Museum is one of London's most iconic venues. Its magnificent architecture and collections create the perfect backdrop for any event. From informal and intimate to creative and spectacular, the Museum's variety of spaces will suit any corporate event, private party or wedding.

Come to our events

Discover the Museum after hours at one of our ticketed events. Whether you want to sleepover, stay up late in a silent disco or hear from one our experts, we have a full programme of events for adults and families now on sale. Please visit our website for more information and to book tickets.

Access for all

The Museum aims to offer the widest possible access to our buildings, events, exhibitions and collections. We are committed to broadening our audiences and developing electronic resources to improve access to the information that our collections contain. We have parking spaces on site for Blue Badge holders and guide dogs are welcome. To find out how we can best accommodate any access requirements please call 020 7942 5000 (during opening hours) or email feedback@nhm.ac.uk or visit nhm.ac.uk/access.

Lots of ways to learn

An exciting mix of daily learning activities for all visitors is on offer. *Investigate*, our hands-on science centre, gives visitors the opportunity to become a scientist. Science Educators help visitors handle, observe and investigate over 300 real Museum specimens, including dinosaur fossils, butterflies and rare minerals. *Nature Live* brings Museum scientists and the public together to discuss the science of nature in the state-of-the-art Attenborough Studio.

Our programme of puppet shows helps young children learn about natural history through familiar fairy tales, and the *Volcanoes and Earthquakes* show offers an immersive theatre experience for the whole family. *Behind-the-scenes Spirit Collection Tours* give visitors a close look at the scale and processes associated with the collections. A variety of self-led printed guides and interactive seasonal workshops are also on offer. Browse daily activities, events and workshops: nhm.ac.uk/whats-on.

Become a volunteer

Are you passionate about the planet? Would you like to help us further our important research and educational mission? There are many invaluable ways in which you can participate, from engaging with visitors in the galleries using real specimens to working on collections-related projects in our cutting-edge science departments and libraries, or maintaining and enhancing the Museum's Wildlife Garden. You can share your skills or learn new ones through a range of short, medium and longer term opportunities. Experience is not always necessary and training is provided. Visit nhm.ac.uk/take-part to find out more and search and apply for vacancies.

Environmental policies

The Museum is committed to continually improving our environmental performance and is accredited to the international standard ISO 14001 for our Environmental Management System. Within this we are focusing on eight key objectives: waste, water, energy, resource use, travel and transport, procurement, biodiversity, and environmental management and communications. We currently produce about 550 tonnes of waste each year, only 2% of which is sent to landfill. However, our strategy is to reduce the amount of waste we produce and resources we use in the first place.

Our non-drinking water comes from our own borehole, reducing the problem of rising groundwater. We installed a highly efficient combined heat and power (CHP) system in 2006 in the central boiler house and we are assessing the carbon impact of any new buildings and refurbishments.

Library and Archives

The Museum's Library and Archives is the world's richest and most comprehensive resource for current and historical natural history literature. Our collections are of international importance, with extensive holdings of early books, journals, electronic resources, artworks, maps and manuscripts. For more information on services, access and opening hours, please call 020 7942 5460 or visit nhm.ac.uk/library.

First published by the Natural History Museum, Cromwell Road, London SW7 5BD
© The Trustees of the Natural History Museum, London 2017. All Rights Reserved.
Reprinted and updated 2018, 2019, 2022.

10 9 8 7

ISBN 978 0 565 09418 8 (English)

Interior design by Bobby Birchall, Bobby&Co.
Reproduction by Saxon Digital Services
Printing by Belmont Press

Picture credits: p26 bottom ©NHM/Kokoro; p30 top ©Geological Society/NHM; p47 ©Longleat Estate; p62 ©GlennV/Shutterstock; p65 top ©Hitesh Oberoi, bottom ©Gagana Mendis Wickramasinghe. All other images are copyright of The Trustees of the Natural History Museum, London. Every effort has been made to accurately credit all copyright-holders. If we have been unsuccessful, we apologise and welcome corrections for future editions and reprints.